FINAL CLUSTERS SOUND EASY!

a phonics **WORKBOOK**

for beginning E.S.L.

students

by sharron bassano

illustrated by craig cornell

The Alemany Press

ISBN 0-88084-200-8

The Alemany Press

Who Is This Book For?

This workbook is created especially for beginning and intermediate adult ESL students of non-academic backgrounds — students who are often mystified by traditional texts, exercise books, and worksheets. Our aim is to provide a medium for listening, speaking, reading, and writing practice of 103 of the most common consonant clusters occurring in the English language in the final position.

We assume that many of our pictures will be easily identified orally by at least some of your students, and we hope that the illustration style and content are interesting to them. Where the meaning of the illustration is not immediately clear (either to your students or to you), we suggest that you use this occurrence to promote conversation among the class members as you try to clarify what the picture is. Remember that "guesswork" or speculation is a talent we are trying to cultivate in our students to help them cope with ambiguous input often encountered in the creative process of learning a second language. (All answers and intentions *are* given in the back of the text, however!)

In this book, you will not find arrows, charts, or diagrams. There are no detailed instructions, complicated spelling rules, or fine print. We have included only the most basic material for two reasons: 1.) Only you, the teacher, can know the best way to ensure comprehension in your students, based on your knowledge of their background, class experiences, and goals. We leave the instruction up to you and your perception of the students' needs and to your particular teaching style. 2.) We intend that our format will allow spelling rules to be inferred and acquired through the plain, uncluttered pages, thereby eliminating the confusion or anxiety often experienced by semi-literate students who are faced with the printed word. This book is aimed at bringing feelings of immediate success and achievement through its easy-to-follow, consistent format, and hopes to encourage study well beyond this introductory experience.

Final Clusters Sound Easy! is the fourth book in our series of phonic/spelling workbooks. The first book, *Consonants Sound Easy,* focuses on introducing the 21 English consonants and the sounds that they most often generate. The second book, *Vowels Sound Easy!,* gives your students recognition of the letters and combinations of letters that generate 11 vowel sounds in English. *Initial Clusters Sound Easy!,* the third book, assists your students with pronunciation and spelling of 26 consonant clusters that begin many English words, but that are not commonly found in other languages. Each of these texts allows the students to work with English sounds in simplified listening, speaking, reading and writing activities at the same time that vocabulary is being augmented.

We hope that your students enjoy and profit from using these workbooks; that they experience their beginnings in reading and writing English in a light-hearted, low-stress way. The following pages will suggest a few ways in which you may use this book; however, we invite you to experiment and expand the activities in any way you see helpful or entertaining, using your special brand of creativity and imagination. Please let us know of your success and concerns.

Sharron Bassano
Craig Cornell

How To Use This Book

Name It!

Wherever pictures are presented, allow your students, as a group, to guess at the vocabulary depicted and at the correct spelling. Use this "brainstorm" time to stimulate conversation. Ask them, "Which ones do we already know?" "Who can tell us what number 8 is?" "Does anyone have any ideas about number 14?" "Yes, I think that is right. . . How shall we spell that one?" etc. As the correct answers are arrived at, write them on the board for all the students to copy in their books. We suggest that as you are writing each word on the board, you give it as much expansion as possible, reminding your students of the contexts in which that item is found. For example, "Yes. . . that *is* a bru*sh*." "What kind of bru*sh* is it?" "A toothbru*sh*. . . shoe bru*sh*. . . oh. . maybe it's a hairbru*sh*." "Do you think it is for bru*sh*ing a dog? I don't know." "Oh, I see. . . it's for fixing your hair. In the bathroom. Maybe it's on the sink." etc.

When all the pictures on a page have been labeled, you might then dictate definitions or sentences to the class as clues and have them tell you which picture you are referring to. For example: "I'm going to work. I'd better fix my hair. . ." ("*Brush!*") "Boy, is this kitchen floor dirty!" ("Wa*sh!*"). If your class is verbal enough, perhaps *they* could give the clues or definitions for each other. Have them make up the context and the answer in pairs, or even have them do the defining or contextualization and *you* guess the word.

Read • Add_____

After your students have had the opportunity to relate a particular spelling configuration (cluster) to a visual image for meaning, they are given a chance to read a list of words containing that cluster as a reinforcement of the spelling pattern and to allow for pronunciation practice. Some of the words they will know the meanings of, others, they may not. Tell them that for the moment, meaning is not important. Suggest that they look carefully at the spelling and practice the sound. Have them read along with you in chorus or in small groups for anonymity in practice. Possibly someone may want to try reading the list solo for the class. Also, you might want to pair the students up asking one to read the list in random order while her/his partner points to the words s/he reads. We personally feel no hesitation in assigning *brief* practice sessions of no-sense words (where the meaning is unknown) for the specific purpose of relating and reinforcing a spelling/pronunciation pattern. After reading down the READ list, have the students write in the missing letters — one at a time, pausing to pronounce the change with each word pair. "Rake" (write in B), "Brake", "Rag" (write in B), "Brag" etc. This practice should be brisk! Obviously, where the difference in meaning is not immediately clear, motivation to distinguish and produce the separate sounds is diminished. Keep it short and lively; move about the room during this practice to be sure that everyone is following along.

Listen • Read • Write

These sections may be handled in two ways, depending on your students' proficiency level.

1.) Ask the students to listen to the sentence as you read it and supply the missing word. They will locate the missing word that you have supplied in either the picture section or in the reading list and write it in the space provided. After completing all sentences, have them check their pages with a partner to see if they have both understood and written the same word. Then you might write the correct words on the board for a final check.

2.) If your group is a little more advanced, you might want to have them just work in pairs or threes trying to decide which word from the pictures or reading list would fit in the space and make sense. Then when they have finished, they could correct their pages together as a whole group in consultation with you.

Review Vocabulary

These pages may be handled in several ways:

1. Do as a group brainstorm as suggested for the NAME IT! sections.

or

2. Write all of the correct words on the blackboard but in a scattered or random order. Students work in pairs to decide which words match which pictures and write them in the book.

or

3. More advanced students might simply work together in pairs or threes helping each other remember the labels and the spellings for each picture based on what they studied only.

or

4. You might want to dictate the label for each picture within a sentence, using the page as a spelling and listening comprehension exercise.

Table of Contents

Final Clusters

Final Clusters

Name it!

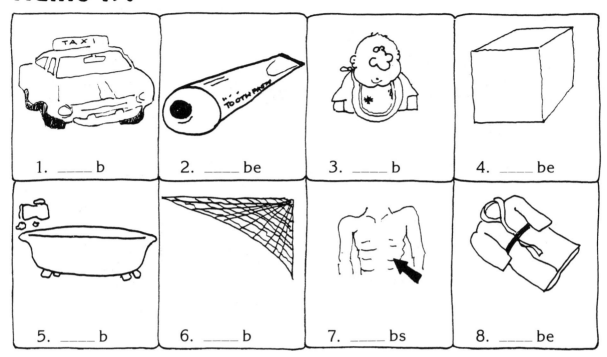

1. ___ b
2. ___ be
3. ___ b
4. ___ be
5. ___ b
6. ___ b
7. ___ bs
8. ___ be

Read	Add _s_	Add _ed_
rob	rob __	robb _____
fib	fib __	fibb _____
robe	robe __	rob _____
mob	mob __	mobb _____
sob	sob __	sobb _____
web	web __	webb _____
cube	cube __	cub _____

Listen • Write • Read

1. Who _____ that bank yesterday?
2. _____ are baby bears.
3. The sugar _____ are on the table.
4. He _____ his tired feet.
5. Please buy 3 _____ of toothpaste.
6. Babies usually wear _____ when they eat.

Name it!

1. ____ p

2. ____ pe

3. ____ p

4. ____ p

5. ____ p

6. ____ p

7. ____ p

8. ____ p

Read	Add __s__	Add __ed__
map	map __	mapp _____
tape	tape __	tap _____
type	type __	typ _____
zip	zip __	zipp _____
slip	slip __	slipp _____
ship	ship __	shipp _____
soap	soap __	soap _____

Listen • Write • Read

1. Where are our _____ of China?

2. She has 3 records and 2 _____.

3. Bill _____ his jacket and went out.

4. How many _____ of coffee did you drink?

5. Mother _____ the floor yesterday.

6. The secretary _____ 40 letters this morning!

Read

1. taps   2. tabs

3. cups   4. cubs

5. mopped   6. mobbed

7. roped   8. robed

9. laps   10. labs

Listen • Write bbed pped ps   bs

1. ro _____   5. zi _____   9. slee _____

2. fi _____   6. soa _____   10. ri _____

3. so _____   7. kee _____   11. mo _____

4. ma _____   8. ru _____   12. ri _____

Listen • Write • Read

1. The cowboy _____ the horse last night.

2. _____ is another word for steals.

3. _____ is another word for cries.

4. When it was cold, she _____ her jacket.

5. Mother _____ her shoes under the bed.

6. He is so thin you can see his _____.

Name it!

1. _____ t

2. _____ te

3. _____ t

4. _____ t

5. _____ t

6. _____ t

7. _____ t

8. _____ t

9. _____ d

10. _____ de

11. _____ d

12. _____ d

13. _____ d

14. _____ d

15. _____ d

16. _____ d

Read

1. pats	4. pads	7. wets	10. weds
2. bets	5. beds	8. pots	11. pods
3. kits	6. kids	9. waits	12. wades

Read

B	P	D	T
1. labs	4. laps	8. lads	12. lats
2. cubs	5. cups	9. cuds	13. cuts
3. ribs	6. rips	10. rids	
	7. beeps	11. beads	14. beets

Listen • Write bs ps ts ds

1. ca _____
2. ma _____
3. ste _____
4. ro _____

5. tu _____
6. sou _____
7. be _____
8. boo _____

9. ligh _____
10. ne _____
11. roa _____
12. bi _____

Listen • Write • Read

1. Use these _____ please.
2. The new _____ are on the table.
3. Where are your fishing _____?
4. What kind of _____ are you cooking?
5. She's not eating the _____.
6. Please put on your _____ because it's raining.
7. Susan and Marta are changing the _____.

Name it!

1. _____ tch   2. _____ tch   3. _____ ch   4. _____ ch

5. _____ ₜch   6. _____ tch   7. _____ ch   8. _____ ch

Read	Add _ed_	Listen • Write • Read
hatch	hatch _____	1. Mother _____ my old jeans.
patch	patch _____	2. Bob never _____ the snake.
watch	watch _____	3. Jack _____ the trailer to the car.
beach	beach _____	4. She _____ football on T.V. with her husband.
reach	reach _____	5. The eggs _____ on Thursday.
hitch	hitch _____	6. She _____ school at 9 o'clock.
touch	touch _____	7. The dog _____ his fleas!
scratch	scratch _____	

[j] [jd]

Name it!

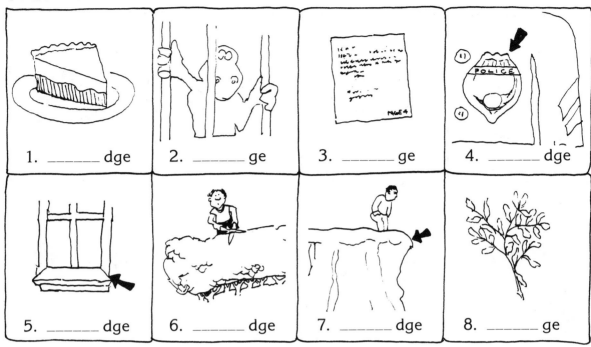

1. _____ dge
2. _____ ge
3. _____ ge
4. _____ dge
5. _____ dge
6. _____ dge
7. _____ dge
8. _____ ge

Read	Add __d__	Listen • Write • Read
rage	rage __	1. The bird was _____.
wedge	wedge __	2. A policeman wears a _____.
cage	cage __	3. Turn to _____ 6 in your book.
edge	edge __	4. Don't stand too near the _____!
siege	siege __	5. A special plant for cooking is _____.
lodge	lodge __	6. Someone who is very angry is "in a _____."
		7. Bushes planted close together are called a _____.

Name it!

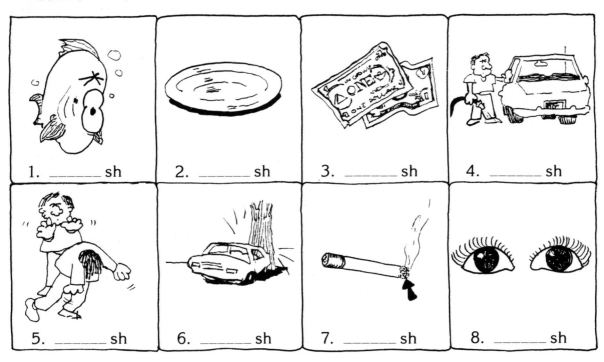

1. _____ sh   2. _____ sh   3. _____ sh   4. _____ sh

5. _____ sh   6. _____ sh   7. _____ sh   8. _____ sh

Read	Add _ed_	Listen • Write • Read
fish	fish ____	1. She _____ the check at the bank on Monday.
dish	dish ____	2. Jack _____ his socks.
cash	cash ____	3. I think she _____ her car into a bus!
wash	wash ____	4. Last summer I _____ in Lake Tahoe.
push	push ____	5. She _____ the baby in the wagon.
crash	crash ____	6. Mother _____ up the dinner.

Read

1. ditched — dished   4. hedged — hatched

2. watched — washed   5. caged — cashed

3. raged — reached   6. paged — pushed

Listen • Write tched ged shed

1. wa _____   5. ca _____   9. di _____

2. wa _____   6. di _____   10. ra _____

3. pu _____   7. pa _____   11. ha _____

4. ca _____   8. cra _____   12. hed _____

Listen • Write • Read

1. Who _____ the T.V. this afternoon?

2. The bird is not _____.

3. He _____ for the money, but he couldn't take it.

4. The eggs _____ yesterday.

5. She _____ her paycheck on Friday.

6. Are his old blue jeans _____?

7. The car didn't start, so the boys _____ it.

8. She _____ her new car.

Review Vocabulary

1. _____

2. _____

3. _____

4. _____

5. _____

6. _____

7. _____

8. _____

9. _____

10. _____

11. _____

12. _____

13. _____

14. _____

15. _____

16. _____

page 10

Name it!

1. _____ g

2. _____ g

3. _____ g

4. _____ g

5. _____ g

6. _____ g

7. _____ g

8. _____ g

Read	Add __s__	Add __ged__
bag	bag __	bag _____
tag	tag __	tag _____
sag	sag __	sag _____
flag	flag __	flag _____
beg	beg __	beg _____
jog	jog __	jog _____
hog	hog __	hog _____

1. Put the _____ in the closet, please.
2. How many _____ are in our yard?!
3. The old bed _____ .
4. The _____ are flying today because it's a holiday.
5. My _____ are tired from standing.
6. The poor man _____ for money on the street.
7. They _____ my suitcase at the airport.
8. She _____ every day. It's good exercise.

Name it!

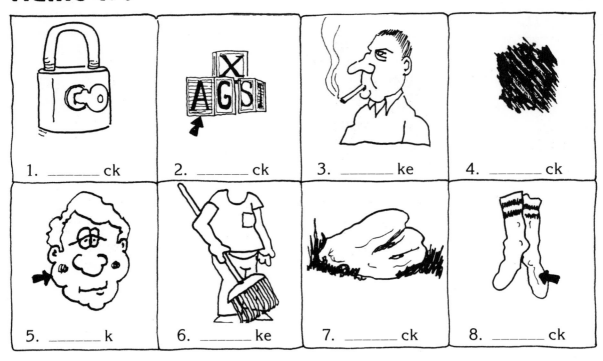

1. _____ ck   2. _____ ck   3. _____ ke   4. _____ ck

5. _____ k   6. _____ ke   7. _____ ck   8. _____ ck

Read	Add _s_	Add _ed_
back	back __	back _____
lock	lock __	lock _____
book	book __	book _____
check	check __	check _____
look	look __	look _____
pick	pick __	pick _____

Listen • Write • Read

1. The girls _____ flowers.
2. The _____ are green and yellow.
3. They _____ their homework.
4. Maria _____ beautiful in her red dress.
5. Grandpa _____ the yard.
6. They always _____ the door.
7. It's too bad that Henry _____.
8. Are these your _____?

page 12

Name it!

1. _____ x   2. _____ x   3. _____ x   4. _____ x

5. _____ x   6. _____ x   7. _____ x   8. _____ x

Read

axe
wax
box
mix
tax

Add ed

ax _____
wax _____
box _____
mix _____
tax _____

Read

text
next

Listen • Write • Read

1. Mother _____ the milk and eggs.
2. The clerk _____ the groceries.
3. Lucy _____ the car.
4. This English _____ book is easy!
5. _____ Monday we are not going to school.
6. Did you pay the _____?
7. She has _____ boy friends!
8. An _____ is a kind of cow.

Read

tags	tagged	tacks	tacked
pegs	pegged	pecks	pecked
bags	bagged	backs	backed

Listen • Write _gs_ _gged_ _cks_ _cked_

1. ta _____   5. pe _____   9. ta _____

2. ba _____   6. ba _____   10. pe _____

3. pe _____   7. ta _____   11. ba _____

4. ta _____   8. ba _____   12. pe _____

Listen • Write • Read

1. The picture is _____ to the wall.

2. The chickens _____ at the corn.

3. Are the price _____ on the shirts?

4. The thumb _____ are in the desk.

5. Will you please carry my _____?

6. The salesman _____ the shoes

7. _____ are small nails made of wood.

8. Uncle Peter _____ his car into the garage.

Name it!

1. _____ f
2. _____ ve
3. _____ fe
4. _____ f
5. _____ f
6. _____ ve
7. _____ ve
8. _____ ve

Read	Add _es_	Read	Add _s_
leaf	leav _____	safe	safe __
knife	kniv _____	roof	roof __
wife	wiv _____	chef	chef __
life	liv _____	love	love __
loaf	loav _____	move	move __
		wave	wave __

Read	Add _ed_	Read	Add _d_
leaf	leaf _____	save	save __
knife	knif _____	love	love __
loaf	loaf _____	live	live __
puff	puff _____	move	move __
roof	roof _____	wave	wave __

Name it!

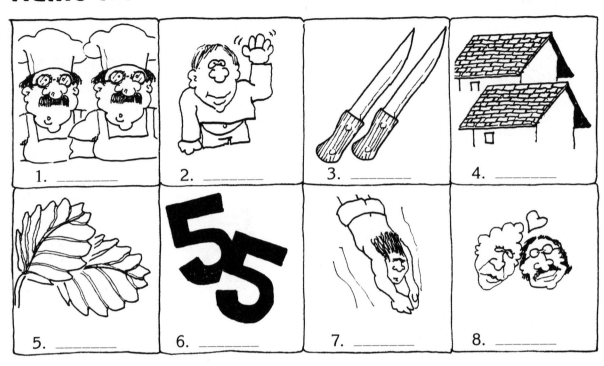

1. _____
2. _____
3. _____
4. _____
5. _____
6. _____
7. _____
8. _____

Listen • Write

1. _____
2. _____
3. _____
4. _____
5. _____
6. _____
7. _____
8. _____

Name it!

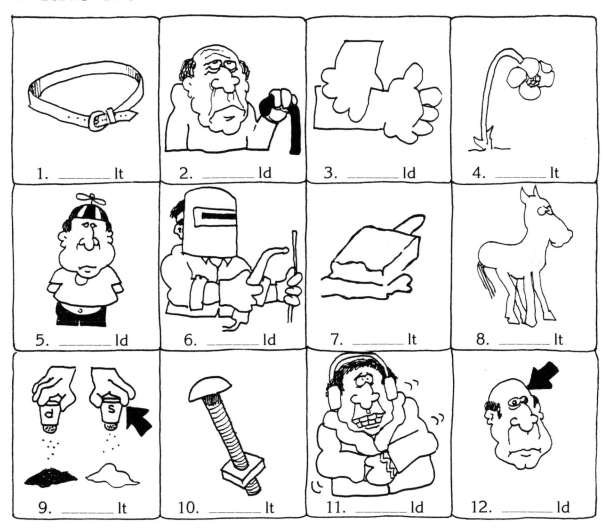

1. _____ lt	2. _____ ld	3. _____ ld	4. _____ lt
5. _____ ld	6. _____ ld	7. _____ lt	8. _____ lt
9. _____ lt	10. _____ lt	11. _____ ld	12. _____ ld

1. cold	4. colt	7. colds	10. colts
2. weld	5. welt	8. welds	11. welts
3. mold	6. molt	9. molds	12. molts

1. Please pass the _____.
2. She bought two _____.
3. The _____ sat on the floor and played.
4. The _____ man has many stories to tell.
5. The _____ are in a small box in the garage.
6. She _____ the baby's hand when he walks.
7. With no water, the flowers _____.

Name it!

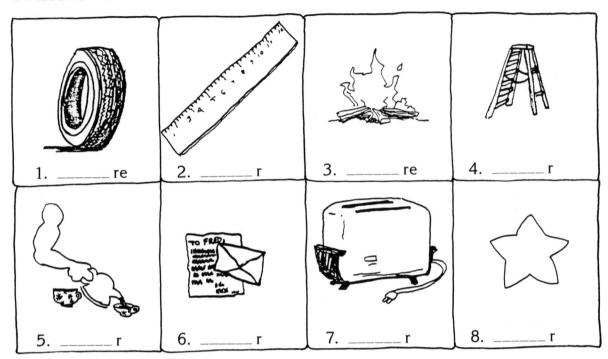

1. _____ re
2. _____ r
3. _____ re
4. _____ r
5. _____ r
6. _____ r
7. _____ r
8. _____ r

Read

star

pour

fire

Add _s_

star __

pour__

fire__

Add _ed_

starr _____

pour _____

fir _____

Listen • Write • Read

1. She wrote two _____ to her sisters.
2. He _____ the coffee into the cup.
3. We need new _____ on the car.
4. They looked at several _____ before they bought one.
5. The students had _____ in their desks.
6. The workers used _____ to pick the apples.
7. There are fifty _____ on the American flag.

page 18

Name it!

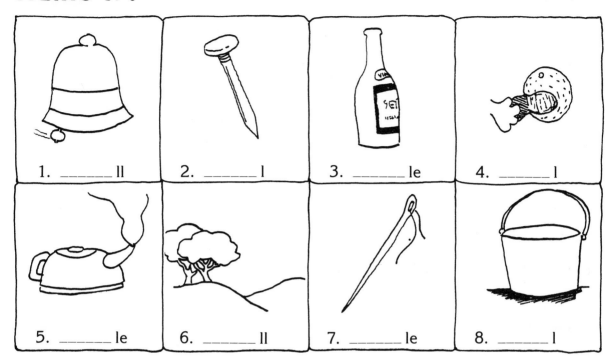

1. _____ ll

2. _____ l

3. _____ le

4. _____ l

5. _____ le

6. _____ ll

7. _____ le

8. _____ l

Read	**Add _s_**	**Add _ed_**
call	call __	call _____
peel	peel __	peel _____
nail	nail __	nail _____
mail	mail __	mail _____
roll	roll __	roll _____

1. The _____ of California are beautiful.

2. She _____ the orange for her son.

3. The boys _____ the ball on the floor.

4. She _____ the letters in the mailbox on the corner.

5. He drank 20 _____ of beer!

6. Where are the _____? I need to fix the table.

7. Grandmother _____ the doctor's office.

8. I can hear the church _____ from my home.

Read

fires	files	fired	filed
stars	stalls	starred	stalled
cars	calls	card	called
roars	rolls	roared	rolled
peers	peels	peered	peeled

Listen • Write rs   ls   red   led

1. fi _____
2. fi _____
3. ca _____
4. pee _____

5. sta _____
6. roa _____
7. fi _____
8. fi _____

9. pee _____
10. roa _____
11. pee _____
12. pee _____

Listen • Write • Read

1. She keeps her papers in the _____.
2. He _____ his mother last night.
3. The monkey _____ the banana.
4. The lion _____ for his dinner.
5. She wrote her name on a _____.
6. Long distance phone _____ cost a lot of money.
7. The business man _____ his reports in the cabinet.
8. There are too many _____ on this freeway!

Review Vocabulary

1. _____

2. _____

3. _____

4. _____

5. _____

6. _____

7. _____

8. _____

9. _____

10. _____

11. _____

12. _____

13. _____

14. _____

15. _____

16. _____

Name it!

1. _____ rt

2. _____ rt

3. _____ rd

4. _____ rd

5. _____ rd

6. _____ rt

7. _____ rd

8. _____ rt

9. _____ rd

10. _____ rt

11. _____ rd

12. _____ rd

herd	herds	hurt	hurts
cord	cords	court	courts
card	cards	cart	carts
ford	fords	fort	forts

1. They painted their name on the _____.
2. You can buy a child's _____ in that store.
3. The tennis _____ are next to the school.
4. The _____ were singing all morining.
5. She drew three _____ on her paper.

Name it!

1. _____ rl
2. _____ rld
3. _____ rl
4. _____ l
5. _____ rl
6. _____ el
7. _____ rl
8. _____ rl

Read	Add _s_	Add _ed_
curl	curl __	curl ____
whirl	whirl __	whirl ____
hurl	hurl __	hurl ____

Listen • Write • Read

1. She has beautiful blond _____.
2. The _____ are full of wine.
3. He _____ the rock across the river.
4. Mrs. Brown has 4 boys and 2 _____.
5. The _____ eat nuts and live in our tree.
6. Her husband bought her a necklace made of _____.

Name it!

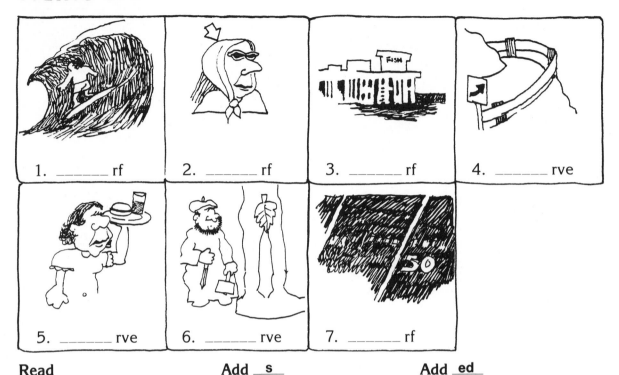

1. _____ rf

2. _____ rf

3. _____ rf

4. _____ rve

5. _____ rve

6. _____ rve

7. _____ rf

Read

curve

carve

serve

surf

* wharf

  scarf

Add s

curve __

carve __

serve __

surf __

wharves

scarves

Add ed

curve __

carve __

serve __

surf __

Listen • Write • Read

1. Some women wear _____ when it is windy.

2. The mountain road is very _____.

3. Let's go fishing on the _____.

4. The grass on a football field is called _____.

5. The waitress _____ the dinner.

6. Father _____ the turkey on the holiday.

page 24

Review Vocabulary

1. _____

2. _____

3. _____

4. _____

5. _____

6. _____

7. _____

8. _____

9. _____

10. _____

11. _____

12. _____

13. _____

14. _____

15. _____

16. _____

Name it!

1. _____ rm
2. _____ rn
3. _____ rm
4. _____ rn
5. _____ rm
6. _____ rm
7. _____ rn
8. _____ rn

Read	Add _s_	Add _ed_
arm	arm __	arm _____
form	form __	form _____
warm	warm __	warm _____
storm	storm __	storm _____
turn	turn __	turn _____
burn	burn __	burn _____

Listen • Write • Read

1. Herman _____ his _____ in the sun.
2. My jacket is _____.
3. There are many _____ in the garden.
4. Luisa made a sweater with yellow _____.
5. The old _____ was painted red.
6. Mother _____ the bread in the oven.
7. It _____ all the month of January.

Name it!

1. _____ rge
2. _____ rch
3. _____ rge
4. _____ rch
5. _____ rch
6. _____ rch
7. _____ rch
8. _____ rch

Read

forge
enlarge
charge
perch
march
search

Add d

forge __
enlarge __
charge __
perche __
marche __
searche __

Listen • Write • Read

1. The children _____ to the music.
2. The bird _____ in the apple tree.
3. Did you _____ for your keys?
4. Yes, I _____ everywhere for them.
5. Do you carry _____ cards in your wallet?
6. The month after February is _____.
7. A photograph that is made bigger is _____.
8. A _____ number of people came to her party.

Name it!

1. _____ rb
2. _____ rb
3. _____ rb

JUMP
DANCE
WORK
CLEAN
DRIVE

4. _____ rp
5. _____ rp
6. _____ rp

Read	**Add _s_**	**Add _ed_**
garb	garb __	garb ___
curb	curb __	curb ___
herb	herb __	
verb	verb __	
harp	harp __	harp ___
tarp	tarp __	
chirp	chirp __	chirp ___
slurp	slurp __	slurp ___

1. Lisa cooked _____ in the soup.
2. We learned 10 new English _____ today.
3. Do you like _____ music?
4. The birds _____ all morning in the sun.
5. He parked the motorcycle next to the _____.
6. Be careful! That knife is _____!
7. He _____ the delicious hot soup!

Name it!

1. _____ rse

2. _____ rse

my little cat
is very fat
he always sat
upon my hat.

3. _____ rse

4. _____ rse

5. _____ rst

6. _____ rst

7. _____ rst

Read	Add _d_	Read	Add _s_
nurse	nurse __	thirst	thirst __
force	force __	burst	burst __
verse	verse __	first	first __
curse	curse __		

Listen • Write • Read

1. The _____ was very kind to her patient.
2. The balloon _____ when the cat played with it.
3. Is this your mother's _____?
4. Is this the _____ time you've visited San Francisco?
5. Shelly writes beautiful English _____.
6. Gene _____ the sick dog for 4 days.

Name it!

1. _____ rk   2. _____ rk   3. _____ rk   4. _____ rk

Read	**Add __s__**	**Add __ed__**
bark	bark __	bark _____
park	park __	park _____
mark	mark __	mark _____
work	work __	work _____
shirk	shirk __	shirk _____

Listen • Write • Read

1. That dog _____ all night!

2. Does it _____ every night?

3. Let's go to the _____.

4. James _____ seven nights a week last month.

5. This month he _____ only five nights.

6. The teacher _____ all the papers "correct".

7. The carpenter _____ his truck in the front yard.

page 30

Review Vocabulary

1. _____

2. _____

3. _____

4. _____

5. _____

6. _____

7. _____

8. _____

9. _____

10. _____

11. _____

12. _____

13. _____

14. _____

15. _____

16. _____

Review Vocabulary

1. _____

2. _____

3. _____

4. _____

5. _____

6. _____

7. _____

8. _____

9. _____

10. _____

11. _____

12. _____

13. _____

14. _____

15. _____

16. _____

Review Vocabulary

1. _____

2. _____

3. _____

4. _____

5. _____

6. _____

7. _____

8. _____

9. _____

10. _____

11. _____

12. _____

13. _____

14. _____

15. _____

16. _____

Review Vocabulary

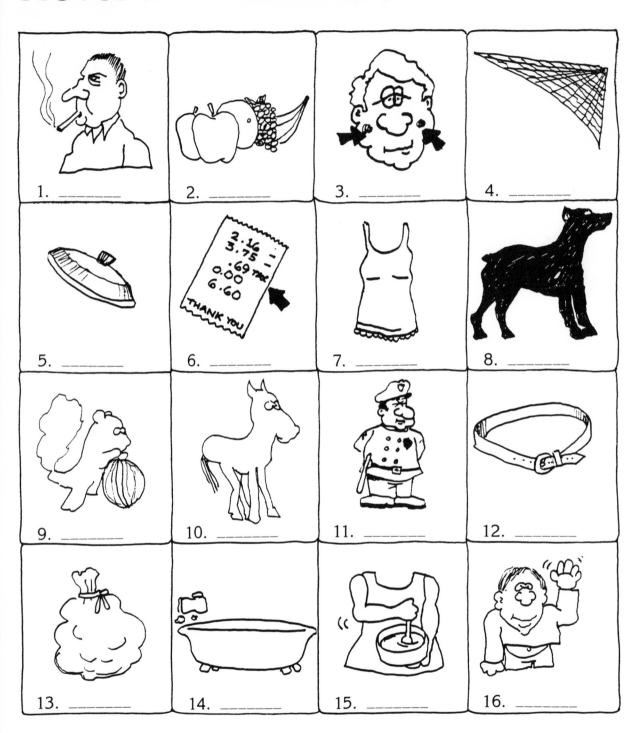

1. _____

2. _____

3. _____

4. _____

5. _____

6. _____

7. _____

8. _____

9. _____

10. _____

11. _____

12. _____

13. _____

14. _____

15. _____

16. _____

Name it!

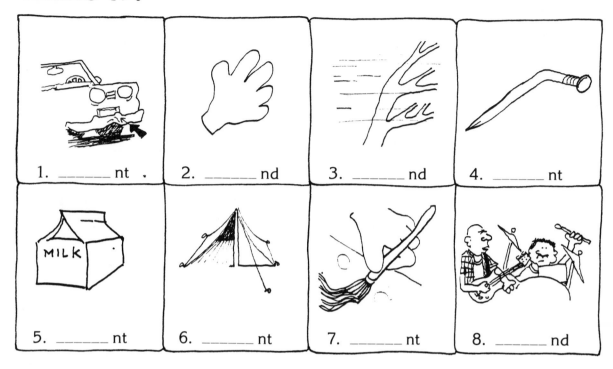

1. _____ nt . 2. _____ nd 3. _____ nd 4. _____ nt

5. _____ nt 6. _____ nt 7. _____ nt 8. _____ nd

Read	Add _s_	Read	Add _s_
pant	pant __	band	band __
dent	dent __	hand	hand __
tint	tint __	wind	wind __
paint	paint __	pond	pond __
pint	pint __	bend	bend __
bent	bent __	land	land __

Listen • Write • Read

1. I like your new _____.
2. Did you go to see that rock and roll _____?
3. He _____ pictures of trees and flowers.
4. Did you wash your _____, Johnnie?
5. Ducks like to swim in _____.
6. Four _____ equal one quart
7. United Airlines flight number 461 _____ at 10 o'clock.
8. Can you _____ over and touch your toes?
9. Her hair is blonde, but she _____ it brown.

page 35

Name it!

1. _____ ns

2. _____ n

3. _____ ne

4. _____ n

5. _____ n

6. _____ ne

7. _____ n

8. _____ ne

9. _____ n

10. _____ n

11. _____ n

12. _____ n

Read	Add _s_	Add _ed_
button	button __	button _____
bone	bone __	bon _____
pin	pin __	pinn _____
fan	fan __	fann _____

1. Lili _____ her sweater when she went outside.

2. The teacher _____ the name tags on the students.

3. Do you eat brown _____ for dinner sometimes?

4. We need _____ in the classroom in July. It's so hot!

5. The dog put all the _____ behind the garage.

6. They _____ their names to the application.

7. Never play with _____!

Name it!

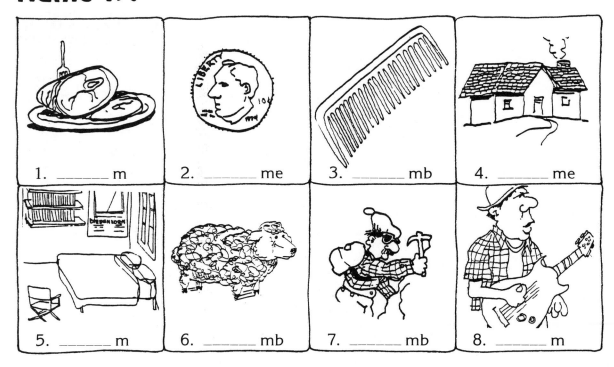

1. _____ m

2. _____ me

3. _____ mb

4. _____ me

5. _____ m

6. _____ mb

7. _____ mb

8. _____ m

Read	Add _s_	Add _ed_
comb	comb __	comb ____
room	room __	room ____
climb	climb __	climb ____
strum	strum __	strumm ____
tame	tame __	tam ____
seem	seem __	seem ____

1. She _____ her daughter's hair for the party.
2. He _____ the lions for the circus.
3. Mrs. Doyle _____ very tired today.
4. Usually she _____ happy!
5. The musician _____ the guitar in the moonlight.
6. The new student _____ her hair in braids.
7. How many _____ do you have in your house?
8. My cat _____ the walnut tree every morning.

Name it!

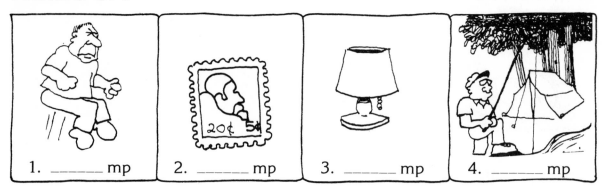

1. _____ mp
2. _____ mp
3. _____ mp
4. _____ mp

Read

pump
camp
jump
stamp
lump
limp

Add _s_

pump __
camp __
jump __
stamp __
lump __
limp __

Add _ed_

pump _____
camp _____
jump _____
stamp _____
lump _____
limp _____

Listen • Write • Read

1. Joe _____ because his foot was hurt.
2. Did you put _____ on the letter?
3. Yes, I _____ it.
4. The children _____ on the bed.
5. Sally and Ron _____ in the mountains together.
6. Ron _____ alone usually.
7. Luis is a mechanic. He _____ gasoline for Texaco.
8. There are too many _____ in my sauce!

Name it!

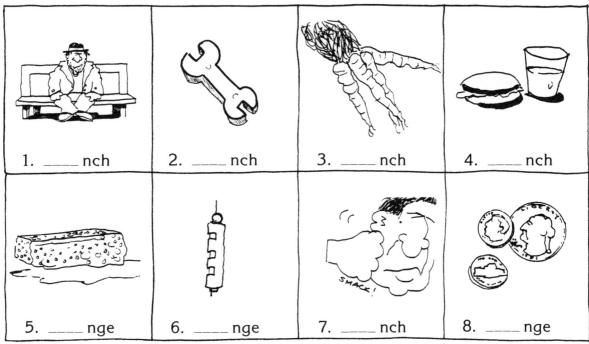

1. _____ nch

2. _____ nch

3. _____ nch

4. _____ nch

5. _____ nge

6. _____ nge

7. _____ nch

8. _____ nge

Read	Add __ed__
munch	munch _____
bunch	bunch _____
lunch	lunch _____
pinch	pinch _____
change	chang _____
hinge	hing _____
sponge	spong _____
lunge	lung _____

Listen • Write • Read

1. The two girls sat on the park _____.

2. Millie likes to take a bath with a _____.

3. The _____ on the closet door is broken.

4. They went to the beach and _____ on hot dogs!

5. Did you eat _____ yesterday?

6. Father had to _____ the tire on the car.

7. Then he _____ his shirt because it was dirty!

Name it!

1. _____ nk
2. _____ ng
3. _____ nk
4. _____ nk
5. _____ nk
6. _____ ng
7. _____ nk
8. _____ ng

Read	**Add s**	**Add ed**
hang	hang __	hang _____
wing	wing __	wing _____
long	long __	long _____
tank	tank __	tank _____
crank	crank __	crank _____
junk	junk __	junk _____
bank	bank __	bank _____

Listen • Write • Read

1. Harry _____ his hat in the hall closet.
2. I bought two _____ at the jewelry store.
3. Lilian _____ at Tommy.
4. She _____ at all the boys!
5. Rosemary sells _____ at the fleamarket.
6. The Wing family _____ to return to Hong Kong.
7. This butterfly has beautiful orange and black _____.
8. Please _____ your towel on the towel rack.

Review Vocabulary

1. _____

2. _____

3. _____

4. _____

5. _____

6. _____

7. _____

8. _____

9. _____

10. _____

11. _____

12. _____

13. _____

14. _____

15. _____

16. _____

Review Vocabulary

1. _____

2. _____

3. _____

4. _____

5. _____

6. _____

7. _____

8. _____

9. _____

10. _____

11. _____

12. _____

13. _____

14. _____

15. _____

16. _____

Review Vocabulary

1. _____

2. _____

3. _____

4. _____

5. _____

6. _____

7. _____

8. _____

9. _____

10. _____

11. _____

12. _____

13. _____

14. _____

15. _____

16. _____

Name it!

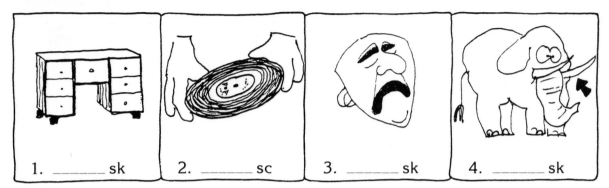

1. _____ sk 2. _____ sc 3. _____ sk 4. _____ sk

Read	Add _s_	Add _ed_
ask	ask __	ask _____
risk	risk __	risk _____
mask	mask __	mask _____
desk	desk __	
disc	disc __	
tusk	tusk __	

Listen • Write • Read

1. Did you _____ a question?

2. Yes, I _____, "What time is it?"

3. Everyone will wear _____ to the party.

4. An elephant has _____, not teeth.

5. Is this your _____?

6. A _____ man robbed the bank.

7. Another name for records is _____.

Name it!

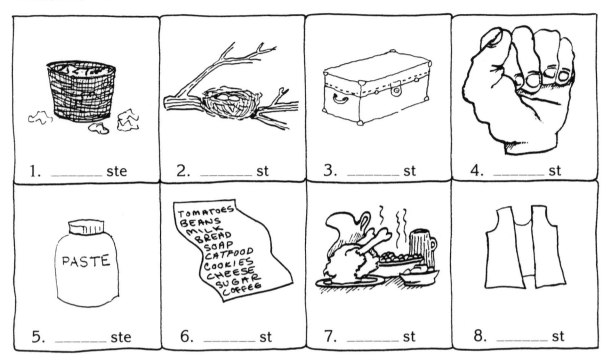

1. _____ ste

2. _____ st

3. _____ st

4. _____ st

5. _____ ste

6. _____ st

7. _____ st

8. _____ st

Read	**Add s **	**Listen • Write • Read**

Read

paste

list

nest

wrist

vest

**Add s **

paste __

list __

nest __

wrist __

vest __

Listen • Write • Read

1. Lucy likes to _____ all the things she needs to buy.

2. She's wearing a gold bracelet on her _____.

3. The birds build small _____ in our orange trees.

4. Mom cooked a _____ on my birthday.

5. A _____ is good to wear on a cold day.

6. I keep my papers in a locked _____.

7. _____ is a kind of glue to stick paper.

8. Sherry threw the letter in the _____ basket.

Name it!

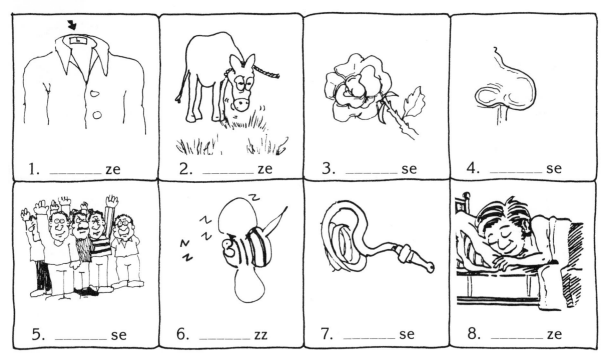

1. _____ ze

2. _____ ze

3. _____ se

4. _____ se

5. _____ se

6. _____ zz

7. _____ se

8. _____ ze

Read	**Add _d_**	**Listen • Write • Read**
size	size __	1. Who _____ the door?
close	close __	2. Who _____ the window?
pose	pose __	3. I was _____ to see her push the car!
raise	raise __	4. She _____ for her photo wearing a red hat.
amaze	amaze __	5. The soldiers _____ the helicopter.
seize	seize __	6. Grandpa _____ off the sidewalk.
		7. Then he _____ off in the arm chair!
		8. The bee _____ around my head.

Review Vocabulary

1. _____

2. _____

3. _____

4. _____

5. _____

6. _____

7. _____

8. _____

9. _____

10. _____

11. _____

12. _____

13. _____

14. _____

15. _____

16. _____

Name it!

1. _____ th
2. _____ th
3. _____ th
4. _____ th
5. _____ th
6. _____ th
7. _____ th
8. _____ the

Read	Add s	Add ed
bathe	bathe __	bathe __
lathe	lathe __	lathe __
breathe	breathe __	breathe __
wreathe	wreathe __	wreathe __
bath	bath __	
path	path __	
math	math __	

1. The _____ goes past the river.
2. I can't do _____ very well.
3. I take a _____ every night.
4. It is hard to _____ when every one is smoking!
5. A _____ is a carpenter's tool.
6. Close the window so the _____ don't fly in!
7. Mother _____ the baby in the sink.
8. The doctor says, "Please _____ deeply."

Review Vocabulary

1. _____
2. _____
3. _____
4. _____
5. _____
6. _____
7. _____
8. _____
9. _____
10. _____
11. _____
12. _____
13. _____
14. _____
15. _____
16. _____

Review Vocabulary

1. _____

2. _____

3. _____

4. _____

5. _____

6. _____

7. _____

8. _____

9. _____

10. _____

11. _____

12. _____

13. _____

14. _____

15. _____

16. _____

Review Vocabulary

1. _____
2. _____
3. _____
4. _____
5. _____
6. _____
7. _____
8. _____
9. _____
10. _____
11. _____
12. _____
13. _____
14. _____
15. _____
16. _____

Final Clusters

Page 1

Name it!

1. cab	2. tube	3. bib	4. cube
5. tub	6. web	7. ribs	8. robe

Listen • Write • Read

1. robbed
2. Cubs
3. cubes
4. rubbed
5. tubes
6. bibs

Page 2

Name it!

1. soap	2. pipe	3. cap	4. ship
5. top	6. cup	7. slip	8. cop

Listen • Write • Read

1. maps
2. tapes
3. zipped
4. cups
5. mopped
6. typed

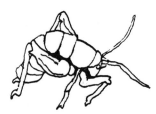

Page 3

Listen and Write

1. robs	5. zips	9. sleeps
2. fibbed	6. soaps	10. ribs
3. sobs	7. keeps	11. mopped
4. mapped	8. rubbed	12. rips

Listen • Write • Read

1. roped
2. Robs
3. Sobs

4. zipped
5. keeps
6. ribs

Page 4

Name it!

1. fruit	2. gate	3. rocket	4. cat
5. net	6. pot	7. light	8. hat
9. lid	10. ride	11. bed	12. seed
13. bread	14. kid	15. bead	16. road

Page 5

Listen and Write

1. cabs	5. tubs	9. lights
2. maps	6. soups	10. nets
3. steps	7. beds	11. roads
4. robs	8. boots	12. bids

Listen • Write • Read

1. mops
2. cups
3. rods
4. soups
5. beets
6. boots
7. beds

Page 6

Name it!

1. scratch	2. latch	3. hatch	4. match
5. watch	6. patch	7. beach	8. peach

Listen • Write • Read

1. patched
2. touched
3. hitched
4. watched
5. hatched
6. reached
7. scratched

Page 7

Name it!

1. wedge   2. cage   3. page   4. badge
5. ledge   6. hedge   7. edge   8. sage

Listen • Write • Read

1. caged
2. badge
3. page
4. edge
5. sage
6. rage
7. hedge

Page 8

Name it!

1. fish   2. dish   3. cash   4. wash
5. push   6. crash   7. ash   8. eyelash

Listen • Write • Read

1. cashed
2. washed
3. crashed
4. fished
5. pushed
6. dished

Page 9

Listen and Write

1. watched   5. cashed   9. dished
2. washed   6. ditched   10. raged
3. pushed   7. paged   11. hatched
4. caged   8. crashed   12. hedged

Listen • Write • Read

1. watched
2. caged
3. reached
4. hatched
5. cashed

6. patched
7. pushed
8. washed

Page 10   Review Vocabulary

Name it!

1. hats	2. caged	3. cubes	4. soaped
5. rides	6. crashed	7. pots	8. cups
9. pushed	10. seeds	11. hedge	12. tubes
13. tops	14. nets	15. beds	16. washed

Page 11

Name it!

1. flag	2. dog	3. bag	4. bug
5. leg	6. tag	7. pig	8. dig

Listen • Write • Read

1. bags
2. dogs
3. sagged
4. flags
5. legs
6. begged
7. tagged
8. jogs

Page 12

Name it!

1. lock	2. block	3. smoke	4. black
5. cheek	6. rake	7. rock	8. sock

Listen • Write • Read

1. picked
2. socks
3. checked
4. looks
5. raked
6. locked
7. smokes
8. books

Page 13

Name it!

1. fox	2. six	3. ox	4. axe
5. wax	6. box	7. mix	8. tax

Listen • Write • Read

1. mixed
2. boxed
3. waxed
4. text
5. Next
6. tax
7. six
8. ox

Page 14

Listen and Write

1. tacked	5. pegs	9. tacks
2. bags	6. bagged	10. pegged
3. pecks	7. tags	11. backed
4. tagged	8. backs	12. pecked

Listen • Write • Read

1. tacked	5. bags
2. pecked	6. tagged
3. tags	7. Pegs
4. tacks	8. backed

Page 15

Name it!

1. chef	2. wave	3. knife	4. roof
5. leaf	6. love	7. five	8. dive

Page 16

Listen and Write

1. Two chefs cooked the dinner.
2. Jack waved good-bye to Susan.

3. Two knives are on the table.
4. The roofs are brown.
5. In October the leaves fall from the trees.
6. She wrote two fives on her paper.
7. He swims and dives well.
8. He has loved her for 15 years.

Page 17

Name it!

1. belt	2. old	3. hold	4. wilt
5. child	6. weld	7. melt	8. colt
9. salt	10. bolt	11. cold	12. bald

Listen • Write • Read

1. salt
2. belts
3. child
4. old
5. bolts
6. holds
7. wilts

Page 18

Name it!

1. tire	2. ruler	3. fire	4. ladder
5. pour	6. letter	7. toaster	8. star

Listen • Write • Read

1. letters
2. poured
3. tires
4. toasters
5. rulers
6. ladders
7. stars

Page 19

Name it!

1. bell	2. nail	3. bottle	4. peel
5. kettle	6. hill	7. needle	8. pail

Listen • Write • Read

1. hills
2. peeled
3. rolled
4. mailed
5. bottles
6. nails
7. called
8. bells

Page 20

Listen and Write

1. fired
2. files
3. cars
4. peeled

5. stars
6. roared
7. filed
8. fires

9. peels
10. roars
11. peers
12. peered

Listen • Write • Read

1. files
2. called
3. peels
4. roared
5. card
6. calls
7. filed
8. cars

Page 21   Review Vocabulary

1. fires
5. bolts
9. nailed
13. weld

2. peeled
6. cold
10. rulers
14. toasters

3. hold
7. hills
11. tires
15. needles

4. poured
8. wilt
12. bells
16. old

*
use in
sentence
for
dictation

Page 22

1. heart
5. herd
9. bird

2. cart
6. hurt
10. court

3. card
7. guard
11. board

4. yard
8. fort
12. sword

Listen ● Write ● Read

1. cards
2. cart
3. courts
4. birds
5. hearts

Page 23

Name it!

1. pearl	2. world	3. girl	4. squirrel
5. curl	6. barrel	7. whirl	8. hurl

Listen ● Write ● Read

1. curls
2. barrels
3. hurled
4. girls
5. squirrels
6. pearls

Page 24

Name it!

1. surf	2. scarf	3. wharf	4. curve
5. serve	6. carve	7. turf	

Listen ● Write ● Read

1. scarves
2. curved
3. wharf
4. turf
5. served
6. carves

Page 25   Review Vocabulary

Name it!   *

1. curled	2. scarves	3. cart	4. boards	use in
5. cards	6. whirled	7. yard	8. girl	sentence
9. served	10. hearts	11. world	12. wharf	for
13. barrels	14. fort	15. curved	16. bird	dictation

Page 26

Name it!

1. arm   2. barn   3. worm   4. yarn
5. storm   6. warm   7. burn   8. torn

Listen • Write • Read

1. burned   arms
2. torn
3. worms
4. yarn
5. barn
6. warms
7. stormed

Page 27

Name it!

1. charge   2. scorch   3. large   4. March
5. perch   6. church   7. torch   8. porch

Listen • Write • Read

1. marched
2. perched
3. search
4. searched
5. charge
6. March
7. enlarged
8. large

Page 28

Name it!

1. curb   2. herb   3. verb
4. harp   5. sharp   6. chirp

Listen • Write • Read

1. herbs
2. verbs
3. harp
4. chirped

5. curb
6. sharp
7. slurped

Page 29

Name it!

1. purse	2. verse	3. horse	4. nurse
5. thirst	6. first	7. burst	

Listen • Write • Read

1. nurse
2. burst
3. purse
4. first
5. verse
6. nursed

Page 30

Name it!

1. bark	2. park	3. work	4. lark

Listen • Write • Read

1. barked
2. bark
3. park
4. worked
5. works
6. marked
7. parked

Page 31

Name it!

1. arm	2. church	3. stormed	4. large	use in
5. torch	6. herb	7. worms	8. chirped	sentence
9. barns	10. herd	11. warmed	12. perched	for
13. guard	14. harps	15. court	16. burned	dictation

*

Page 32   Review Vocabulary

Name it!

1. edge	2. cap	3. rakes	4. bibbed

5. dish	6. wedge	7. gate	8. digs	* use in sentence for dictation
9. cat	10. robed	11. kettle	12. paged	
13. shipped	14. pearl	15. March	16. locked	

Page 33   Review Vocabulary

Name it!

1. ledge	2. rockets	3. cab	4. pipe	use in
5. blacked	6. torn	7. flagged	8. ribs	sentence
9. child	10. badge	11. boxed	12. lights	for
13. leg	14. fished	15. sword	16. cashed	dictation

Page 34   Review Vocabulary

Name it!

1. smokes	2. fruits	3. cheeks	4. webbed
5. lid	6. taxed	7. slip	8. dog
9. squirrel	10. colt	11. cop	12. belts
13. bagged	14. tub	15. mixed	16. waved

Page 35

Name it!

1. dent	2. hand	3. wind	4. bent
5. pint	6. tent	7. paint	8. band

Listen • Write • Read

1. pants
2. band
3. paints
4. hands
5. ponds
6. pints
7. lands
8. bend
9. tints

Page 36

Name it!

1. beans	2. gun	3. cone	4. button
5. chicken	6. bone	7. pin	8. cane
9. fan	10. sign	11. pen	12. ten

Listen • Write • Read

1. buttoned
2. pinned
3. beans
4. fans
5. bones
6. signed
7. guns

Page 37

Name it!

1. ham	2. dime	3. comb	4. home
5. room	6. lamb	7. climb	8. strum

Listen • Write • Read

1. combed
2. tamed
3. seemed
4. seems
5. strummed
6. combs
7. rooms
8. climbs

Page 38

Name it!

1. jump	2. stamp	3. lamp	4. camp

Listen • Write • Read

1. limped
2. stamps
3. stamped
4. jumped
5. camped
6. camps
7. pumps
8. lumps

Page 39

Name it!

1. bench　　2. wrench　　3. bunch　　4. lunch
5. sponge　　6. hinge　　7. punch　　8. change

Listen • Write • Read

1. bench
2. sponge
3. hinge
4. munched
5. lunch
6. change
7. changed

Page 40

Name it!

1. tank　　2. ring　　3. ink　　4. junk
5. sink　　6. sing　　7. wink　　8. swing

Listen • Write • Read

1. hangs
2. rings
3. winked
4. winks
5. junk
6. longs
7. wings
8. hand

Page 41　　Review Vocabulary

Name it!

				*
1. beans	2. band	3. tens	4. wind	use in
5. pinned	6. hand	7. sings	8. paints	sentence
9. pint	10. bent	11. comb	12. camps	for
13. lamp	14. junk	15. stamp	16. buttoned	dictation

Page 42　　Review Vocabulary

Name it!

1. winked　　2. bottled　　3. tank　　4. rock

5. signs   6. penned   7. cones   8. tent

9. axed   10. dives   11. homes   12. sink

13. melts   14. fox   15. ring   16. arm

*
use in
sentence
for
dictation

Page 43   Review Vocabulary

Name it!

1. tagged   2. ox   3. dimes   4. bald

5. jumped   6. hens   7. bones   8. ladders

9. socks   10. pigs   11. yarn   12. child

13. inked   14. pails   15. fanned   16. six

Page 44

Name it!

1. desk   2. disc   3. mask   4. tusk

Listen • Write • Read

1. ask
2. asked
3. masks
4. tusks
5. desk
6. masked
7. discs

Page 45

Name it!

1. waste basket   2. nest   3. chest   4. fist

5. paste   6. list   7. feast   8. vest

Listen • Write • Read

1. list
2. wrist
3. nests
4. feast
5. vest
6. chest
7. Paste
8. waste

Page 46

Name it!

1. size	2. graze	3. rose	4. nose
5. raise	6. buzz	7. hose	8. doze

Listen • Write • Read

1. closed
2. raised
3. amazed
4. posed
5. seized
6. hosed
7. dozed
8. buzzed

Page 47   Review Vocabulary

Name it!

*

1. desks	2. list	3. masked	4. fist	use in
5. tusks	6. waste	7. vests	8. washed	sentence
9. nests	10. push	11. disc	12. paste	for
13. fished	14. buzzed	15. crashed	16. dish	dictation

Page 48

Name it!

1. moth	2. math	3. bath	4. path
5. north	6. south	7. mouth	8. lathe

Listen • Write • Read

1. path
2. math
3. bath
4. breathe
5. lathe
6. moths
7. bathes
8. breathe

Page 49   Review Vocabulary

Name it!

1. bagged	2. nailed	3. mix	4. crash

5. holds	6. bugs	7. caged	8. digs
9. webbed	10. cheeks	11. cashed	12. pipe
13. box	14. rides	15. fox	16. masked

* use in sentence for dictation

Page 50   Review Vocabulary

Name it!

1. curved	2. pushed	3. hurl	4. bottled
5. pint	6. flagged	7. fish	8. robed
9. raked	10. scarf	11. socks	12. seeds
13. jumps	14. band	15. shipped	16. poured

* use in sentence for dictation

Page 51   Review Vocabulary

Name it!

1. tusks	2. smoked	3. dished	4. buzzed
5. belt	6. wash	7. hams	8. lark
9. tagged	10. ribs	11. wedge	12. soaps
13. locked	14. fruits	15. six	16. court